How to SURVI~~ the SATs Writing 7~~

G000116066

- You've got TWO writing tests to do for the SAT.
  For each one you've got to do a different type of writing.

- There's a whole bunch of different types of writing that could
  come up. This book gives you practice for a load of them.
  The rest of them are in the other workbooks.

- The fancy flap at the back of this book has got the Rules for each
  type of writing. When you start a question, fold out the flap and read
  through the rules for the writing you're doing.

- Each question in this book gives you a writing grid for planning —
  just like the real SAT tests. We've stuck in ideas to get your brain
  working. Read our ideas and then come up with ideas of your own.

- Pick the best ideas, plan your writing and write it — then make a
  bazillion quid by selling it to Hollywood. (This last bit is optional)

Are you going to Writing Wonderland
or Writing Blunderland?

AL-KHAIR FOUNDATION
109-117 CHERRY ORCHARD ROAD
CROYDON SURREY CR0 6BE

Year 6 HAVE to do SATs, whether they like it or not

Writing's one of the toughest things kids have to do in the SATs.
We think they'll do better if they understand exactly what they're being asked to do.

In our <u>Writing Rules</u> book we explain how to do each type of writing that could come up in the SAT and give clear examples of how to get it right.

The <u>Workbooks</u> give kids loads of <u>practice</u> on all the types of writing covered in <u>Writing Rules</u>:

THIS BOOK

WORKBOOK 1 — FICTION WRITING

- HORROR STORIES
- ADVENTURE STORIES
- FABLES
- STORIES WITH FLASHBACKS
- FANTASY ADVENTURES
- PLAY SCRIPTS
- STORIES WITH A FAMILIAR SETTING

WORKBOOK 3 — NON-FICTION WRITING

- FACTUAL REPORTS
- LETTERS TO FRIENDS AND FAMILY
- FORMAL LETTERS
- ADVERTS, FLYERS
- DIARIES
- DISCUSSING ISSUES
- WRITING ABOUT YOUR POINT OF VIEW

WORKBOOK 2 — FICTION WRITING

- STORIES THAT RAISE ISSUES
- MYSTERY STORIES
- CONVERSATIONS
- HISTORICAL STORIES
- SCIENCE FICTION STORIES
- HUMOROUS STORIES
- STORIES WITH A DILEMMA
- STORIES WITH A TWIST

WORKBOOK 4 — NON-FICTION WRITING

- WRITING AN ARGUMENT
- RECOUNTING EVENTS
- ARTICLES
- BIOGRAPHIES
- NEWSLETTERS
- INSTRUCTIONS
- DESCRIPTIONS
- EXPLANATIONS

Here's how it works...

1) Make sure the whole class knows that:
   - the point of this book is to GET INTO WRITING WONDERLAND and stay in.
   - you stay in Wonderland by _meeting targets_.

2) Use the 'Writing Rules' book to go over the style of writing you want to cover.

3) Read through the question. Get the kids to use the boxes on the left-hand page to generate ideas, then plan their work using the writing frame on the right.

4) Set the kids targets for writing up their answers. You can base them on the rules printed on the folding page at the back of this book. We've left a space where you can write the target at the bottom of each right-hand page.

5) If a child meets their target, they're in Writing Wonderland, but if they miss one they go to Writing Blunderland — until next time they meet their targets.

6) You could circle the Wonderland or Blunderland picture at the top of each page to show whether they've met their targets.

7) Even better, make a massive poster, with stickers for the kids' names. Stick the names in Wonderland or Blunderland in a weekly ceremony. Give prizes for going to Wonderland and punishments for going to Blunderland — maybe trimming all the grass at the local park with nose-hair trimmers, or, more realistically, doing the page again for homework...

Section 1 — Factual Reports

Factual Reports — 1

Factual reports inform people about events in a clear, straightforward way.
Avoid humour, informal language and any mention that factual reports are a bit boring.

Your class has just been taken on a trip to the zoo to learn about wild animals.

Write a factual report about your class' day out at the zoo.

You will need to decide:

• When and where you went

• What important things you saw and did there

• What the class learnt

Think about your report and scribble down your extra ideas in the boxes...

THINGS YOU DID AT THE ZOO

did sketches
of animals

listened to
a talk

group discussion

took notes

THINGS YOU SAW AT THE ZOO

fruit bats

lions being fed

lemurs running free
around the zoo

apes

WHAT YOU LEARNT

what kinds of
animals live in water

how animals are adapted to
living in different environments

how humans are
related to apes

WHAT THE DAY OUT WAS LIKE OVERALL

enjoyable

informative

learnt a lot
about animals

a good day out

Factual Reports — 1

Choose the best ideas from over the page and fill in the writing frame below.

When and **where** did the class go to visit the zoo? ....

....

What important things did you **do** and **see** there?

What did the class **learn**?

What is the conclusion?

*Rules for writing fantastic **factual reports** are on the flap at the back.*
Read the rules — then use your plan to write a report that's crammed full of facts.
Get ☐ *rules right in your report for a free pass to Writing Wonderland.*

Factual Reports — 2

Not more ultra-boring, scummy, "Why me?" factual reports? Oh nooooo! Oh yes.

> **Write a factual report about your school's sports day.**
>
> You will need to include:
> • When and where the sports day took place
> • What sporting events took place during the day
> • Who won the main races and how the prizes were given out

Factual reports aren't that bad really.
Fill in some extra ideas in the spaces below and you'll have this one cracked in no time.

SPORTING EVENTS TO INCLUDE

relay race   hurdles

obstacle race

100 metres race

sack race

WHO WON THE MAIN RACES

John Le Motty

Deepak Chaudry

Deborah Lord   Steven Almond

Louise Meacock

HOW THE PRIZES WERE GIVEN OUT

winners got chocolate / badges

there was a small ceremony

the headteacher gave out prizes

it was at the end of the day

WHAT THE DAY WAS LIKE OVERALL

FINISH

many different sporting events
everyone enjoyed it
everyone took part in a race

Factual Reports — 2

Pick your favourite ideas from over the page and fill in the writing frame below.

Where and **when** did the sports day take place? ....

....

What **sporting events** took place?

Who won the main races? How were the prizes given out?

What is your conclusion about what the sports day was like?

*Rules for writing fantastic **factual reports** are on the flap at the back.*
Read the rules — then use your plan to write a report that's crammed full of facts.

Get ☐ rules right in your report for a free pass to Writing Wonderland.

Factual Reports — 3

Crikey — the last factual report question in the book. Make it a good one.

Write a factual report about a school play.

You will need to think about:

• What the play was

• How pupils prepared to put on the play

• Where and when the play was performed

• Whether the audience liked the play

You know the drill — scribble some extra ideas down in the boxes below.

TYPES OF PLAY

Nativity play

pantomime

musical

drama

PREPARATIONS FOR THE PLAY

casting parts

making costumes

rehearsing the play

POSSIBLE PLACES AND TIMES

in school hall

local village hall

summer term

Thursday evening

DID THE PLAY GO WELL?

the audience enjoyed it

the performance was good

the pupils liked performing

Factual Reports — 3

Use your best ideas from over the page to do a more detailed plan in the writing frame below. Then you'll be able to polish off the report in no time.

What **type of play** was put on? ....

....

How did pupils **prepare** for the play?

When and **where** was the play performed? ....

....

Did the **audience** like the play? ....

....

What is your **conclusion** about the play?

*Rules for writing fantastic **factual reports** are on the flap at the back.*
Read the rules — then use your plan to write a report that's crammed full of facts.

Get ☐ *rules right in your report for a free pass to Writing Wonderland.*

Letters To Friends And Family — 1

You'll have no excuse not to write to your Grandma after this...

Imagine you have just got back from a foreign holiday.

Write a letter to your Grandma that tells her all about it.

You will need to think about:

- Where you have been
- The three most exciting things that happened while you were there
- Who you went with
- How you are going to begin and end your letter

Write some extra ideas for the letter in these boxes.
You can make them as wacky as you like.

WHO YOU WENT WITH

your mum and dad   your school

Atomic Kitten

HOLIDAY LOCATIONS

Honolulu

Florida

Switzerland

Butlins

THINGS THAT MIGHT HAVE HAPPENED

your passport got eaten by sharks

a jellyfish stole your sandals

you met David Beckham on the beach

HOW TO END THE LETTER

I'll send you some photos when we get them

See you in a few weeks

I hope to see you soon

Letters To Friends And Family — 1

Use your ideas from the last page to fill in this writing frame.

How will you **start** the letter? ....

....

Where have you been on your holiday?

What three things happened while you were on holiday?

Who was with you on holiday?

How will you **end** your letter? ....

....

....

*Rules for writing lovely **letters to friends and family** are on the flap at the back.
Read the rules — then use your plan to write a letter that'll get you in the good books.*

Get ☐ *rules right in your letter for a free pass to Writing Wonderland.*

Letters To Friends And Family — 2

Dear me — here's another letter for you to write.

Imagine you have just moved house and had to change school.

**Write a letter to your cousin telling her about
your new house and new school.**

You will need to decide:

• What your new house and school are like

• Whether you like it there or not

• If you have made any new friends, and what they are like

*Put all your extra ideas in these boxes.
Remember you're writing to someone you know.*

WORDS TO DESCRIBE YOUR HOUSE

messy   cold

friendly   homely

WAYS TO DESCRIBE YOUR NEW SCHOOL

big   scary

welcoming

HOW YOU MIGHT BE FEELING

excited

nervous

miserable

lonely

PHRASES TO END YOUR LETTER WITH

All my love

Write soon

See you next week

Letters To Friends And Family — 2

Use your ideas to plan your letter here. Try and keep your writing friendly and informal.

What is the **first sentence** of your letter?

....

How do you **feel** about moving?

....

What is your new **house** like?

What do you think of your new school?

What new friends have you made?

What **sentence** and **phrase** will you use to **end** your letter?

*Rules for writing lovely **letters to friends and family** are on the flap at the back.*
Read the rules — then use your plan to write a letter that'll get you in the good books.

Get ⬚ *rules right in your letter for a free pass to Writing Wonderland.*

Letters To Friends And Family — 3

One final letter to have a go at — make sure you make it interesting to read.

Imagine that it is your best friend's birthday next week. You are planning
a surprise party, but need some help getting things organised secretly.

**Write a letter to one of your other friends telling them
about the party and asking for their help.**

You will need to decide:

- When the party will be
- Where the party will be held
- What you have planned
- What you want your friend to do

Write down all your ideas for the party.
Think about how you are going to keep your plans a secret.

WHERE THE PARTY COULD BE HELD

your house

the beach

swimming pool

EVENTS AT THE PARTY

a visit from your best friend's favourite band

a magician

THINGS FOR YOUR FRIEND TO DO

keep your best friend busy just before the party

help blow up balloons

SENTENCES TO END YOUR LETTER WITH

Remember — not word to anyone

Thanks for your help — I couldn't do it without you

Letters To Friends And Family — 3

Use this writing grid to plan your letter.

What is the **first sentence** of your letter? ....

....

Where and **when** will the party be held?

What activities / events do you have planned for the party?

What do you want your friend to **do to help**?

What **sentence** and **phrase** will you use to **end** your letter?

---

*Rules for writing lovely **letters to friends and family** are on the flap at the back.*
Read the rules — then use your plan to write a letter that'll get you in the good books.

Get ☐ *rules right in your letter for a free pass to Writing Wonderland.*

Formal Letters — 1

No more informality... this time you've got to write a __formal__ letter.

The local council is planning to build a new shopping arcade on the park, but it needs to know the opinions of local people. The swings, pond and football pitches will be replaced with new shops, a cinema and a large car park.

Write a formal letter to your local council saying whether you agree or disagree with the plans.

You will need to consider:

• Who will be affected by the plans

• Who will benefit from the plans and who will lose out

• Whether the whole community will benefit or lose out

Try and keep all your points clear.

BAD POINTS

neighbourhood will be less attractive

will lose a local play area

PEOPLE WHO MIGHT LOSE OUT

local children who play in the park

people who walk their dogs there

joggers

GOOD POINTS

people will have a local cinema

won't have to travel as far to the shops

PEOPLE WHO MIGHT BENEFIT

young people in the area

busy people who need easy access to shops

Formal Letters — 1

Fill in this writing frame below — remember to start and end the letter properly.

How will you begin your letter? ....

....

....

Who will be **affected** by the plans?

Who will **benefit** from the plans?

Who will **lose out** because of the plans?

Do you think the plans are a good idea overall?

How will you **end** the letter? ....

....

....

*Rules for writing fabulous **formal letters** are on the flap at the back.*
Read the rules — then use your plan to write an oh-so-serious letter.
Get ⬚ rules right in your letter for a free pass to Writing Wonderland.

Formal Letters — 2

Formal letters don't always have to be complaints...

You are planning a holiday in the Lake District with your family.

**Write a formal letter to a hotel to book rooms
for you and your family.**

You will need to consider:

• How many rooms you will need

• How many nights you will need the rooms for

• Any special requirements

*Write down all your ideas in the boxes below.
You need to be very clear about what you are asking for.*

WAYS TO START THE LETTER

I would like to reserve rooms for...

I am looking for accommodation...

DIFFERENT TYPES OF ROOM

single   double

family room

with bathroom

SPECIAL REQUIREMENTS

your sister is vegetarian

need wheelchair access

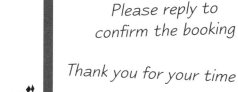

WAYS TO END THE LETTER

Please reply to confirm the booking

Thank you for your time

Formal Letters — 2

Use the writing frame below to plan your letter.

How will you **start** the letter? ....

....

....

When do you want the rooms and for **how long**?

How many rooms do you need, and what **type of room**?

What **special requirements** do you have?

How will you **end your letter**? ....

....

....

*Rules for writing fabulous **formal letters** are on the flap at the back.*
Read the rules — then use your plan to write an oh-so-serious letter.
Get ☐ *rules right in your letter for a free pass to Writing Wonderland.*

Formal Letters — 3

You can use a formal letter to ask for information.

Imagine you are doing some research for a school project.
You need to find out about recycling in your area.

**Write a formal letter to your local council
asking for help with your research.**

You will need to decide:

- How you will start your letter
- What three questions you will ask
- How you will end your letter

Write down all your ideas here.

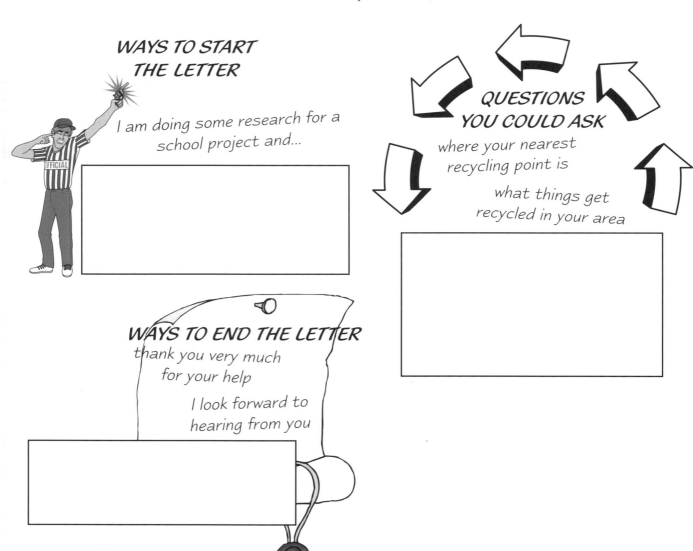

WAYS TO START THE LETTER

I am doing some research for a school project and...

QUESTIONS YOU COULD ASK

where your nearest recycling point is

what things get recycled in your area

WAYS TO END THE LETTER

thank you very much for your help

I look forward to hearing from you

Formal Letters — 3

Plan your letter using this writing frame.
Remember to thank the reader at the end of your letter.

How will you **start** your letter? ....

....

....

Which **three pieces of information** will you ask for?

How will you **end your letter**? ....

....

....

*Rules for writing fabulous **formal letters** are on the flap at the back.*
Read the rules — then use your plan to write an oh-so-serious letter.

Get ☐ rules right in your letter for a free pass to Writing Wonderland.

Formal Letters — 4

You guessed it, it's another formal letter.

There is a piece of grassy land near your house that belongs to the local council. It used to be a playground, but now it's covered in weeds, and nobody uses it. You and a group of friends want to make it useful again.

Write a formal letter to your local council explaining your ideas for the playground and asking for support with the project.

You will need to consider:

- What you plan to do with the piece of land
- Who will benefit from your plans
- What you need from the council

Put all your ideas in the boxes below.

THINGS TO DO WITH THE LAND

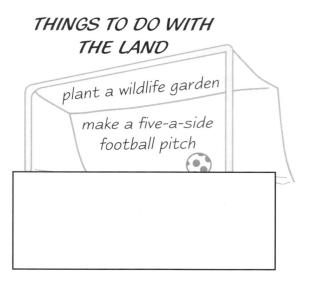

plant a wildlife garden

make a five-a-side football pitch

WHO MIGHT BENEFIT

local children

local wildlife

WHAT YOU MIGHT NEED FROM THE COUNCIL

just permission to use the land

some money to pay for seeds

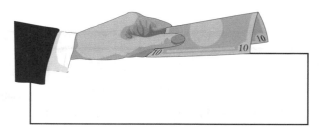

WHY THE COUNCIL SHOULD SAY YES

it would make a real difference to the community

you and your friends are offering to work for free

Formal Letters — 4

Plan your letter here.
Remember to keep all your points clear, and start a new paragraph for each new point.

How will you **start** your letter? ....

....

....

What do you **plan to do** with the piece of land?

What do you need from the council?

Why should the council **agree**?

*Rules for writing fabulous **formal letters** are on the flap at the back.*
Read the rules — then use your plan to write an oh-so-serious letter.

Get ☐ *rules right in your letter for a free pass to Writing Wonderland.*

Section 4 — Adverts And Flyers

Adverts And Flyers — 1

This is really worth getting good at — people who work in advertising get paid a fortune.

Stink-Go soap company are bringing out a new type of soap, designed for children.

Design a flyer for the new soap, that will make children really want to buy it.

You will need to decide:

- What is special about the soap
- How you'll make children want to buy it
- How to lay out the flyer

Think up some really attention-grabbing ideas for your flyer and stick them down here.

WHAT THE SOAP'S CALLED

Super Soap

Wishy Washy

Imperial Heather

WHAT'S SO GREAT ABOUT THE SOAP

makes you fly

smells great

smells of bubblegum

WHY CHILDREN WILL WANT TO BUY THE SOAP

will make them look cool

will make parents happy

free chocolate with every bar

CATCHY WORDING

cheap as chips

you're worth it

unbelievable results

Adverts And Flyers — 1

Write down your best and brightest ideas here, ready to use in your flyer.

What is the soap called?

What's special about the soap?

How will you make children
want to **buy** the soap?

What else will you need
to put in the flyer?

*Rules for writing amazing **adverts** are on the flap at the back.*
Read the rules — then use your plan to write an advert that could sell ice to an eskimo.

Get ☐ rules right in your advert for a free pass to Writing Wonderland.

Adverts And Flyers — 2

Sell, sell, sell! Make your readers really <u>want</u> the thing you're describing.

Your school has decided to offer a salad bar at lunchtime
as an alternative to ordinary school meals.

Write a flyer advertising the salad bar to pupils and teachers.

You will need to decide:

- What the salad bar is like and what's good about it
- How to make it sound exciting
- How to lay out the flyer

Get your brain crunching on a few ideas for the flyer and stick 'em down here.

CATCHY WORDING

scrumptious salads

you'll be BURSTING
with health

tasty treats

Adverts And Flyers — 2

Salad... yum... But chips are nicer, so you'll need to make this salad bar sound really great.

Who can buy lunch at the salad bar? ....

....

What are the **opening times**? ....

....

What will be sold at the salad bar?	**What** will you say to **persuade** people to eat at the salad bar?

How will you **lay out** the flyer?

*Rules for writing amazing **adverts** are on the flap at the back.*
Read the rules — then use your plan to write an advert that could sell ice to an eskimo.
Get ☐ *rules right in your advert for a free pass to Writing Wonderland.*

Adverts And Flyers — 3

*It's easy to make cool stuff sound cool. It's much tougher to persuade
people to do something that could be a bit embarrassing...*

A teacher at your school has decided to have her head shaved to raise money
for the local hospital. She wants to persuade parents of pupils at your school
to shave their heads too, so that even more money can be raised.

**Write a flyer which will be sent home to parents,
persuading them to join in with the charity head-shaving.**

You will need to decide:

- When and where the head-shaving event will take place
- How to persuade parents to join in
- What to tell parents about the charity they will be helping
- How to lay out the flyer

*Hmmm... persuading my mum to have her head shaved would be tricky.
My dad might say yes, though — he's half-bald already.*

WHY PARENTS WON'T WANT TO DO IT

shy   busy
embarrassed

REASONS WHY PARENTS WILL ENJOY THE EVENT

live band   free food

fun to watch others
being shaved

CATCHY WORDING

beautiful bald bonce

We need YOUR help...   feel the wind in
your stubble

WHY PARENTS SHOULD HELP RAISE MONEY

feels good to help others

hospital needs a
new incubator   save lives

Adverts And Flyers — 3

Pin your ideas down in the frame below. Get all your thinking done here
— then when you get onto the writing it'll be no sweat.

When and where will the head-shaving event take place?

Why should parents join in?

What else will you tell parents in the flyer?

*Rules for writing amazing **adverts** are on the flap at the back.*
Read the rules — then use your plan to write an advert that could sell ice to an eskimo.
Get ☐ *rules right in your advert for a free pass to Writing Wonderland.*

Section 5 — Diaries

Diaries — 1

Wednesday 23rd April, 2008 — had to write a diary as part of my SATs preparation. Poo.

Write a diary that tells the story of an important time in your life.

You will need to decide:

- How many days to include in your diary
- Why this time in your life is important
- How you feel about the event
- How to express your emotions in the diary

Write your ideas for the diary in the boxes below.
Remember to think of emotions as well as events.

EVENTS TO WRITE ABOUT

a competition   birthday

a pet dying   moving house

POSSIBLE EMOTIONS

anger

fear

excitement

depression

OTHER CHARACTERS

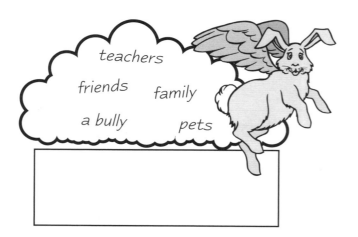

teachers

friends   family

a bully   pets

TIME PERIODS

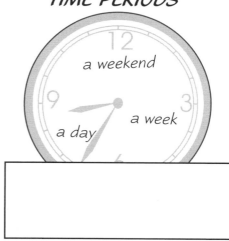

a weekend

a week

a day

Diaries — 1

Now use your best ideas from over the page to fill in this writing frame.

What event have you chosen to write about?

How many days will your diary last?

What is important about this event?

What emotions do you feel?

*Rules for writing dramatic **diaries** are on the flap at the back.*
Read the rules — then use your plan to write a very revealing diary.

Get ☐ rules right in your diary for a free pass to Writing Wonderland.

Diaries — 2

*Confiding your personal thoughts to the examiner is a bit weird —
but that's what diary writing's all about.*

Write a diary about a small accident that happened to you.

You will need to decide:

• What kind of accident happens

• How you feel during the accident

• What happens after the accident, e.g. you get better

• How many days the diary covers

Phew — this SAT question is a bit grim. All the better to test you with, my dear...

SMALL ACCIDENTS

burning fingers

falling over on skateboard

bitten by guinea pig

injured playing football

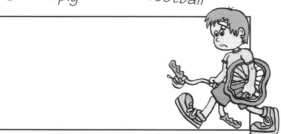

WORDS TO DESCRIBE HOW YOU FEEL DURING THE ACCIDENT

frightened   shocked

hurt

worried

PEOPLE WHO LOOK AFTER YOU AFTER THE ACCIDENT

your mum or dad

your sister

doctor   a friend

POSSIBLE AFTER-EFFECTS

off school for three days

small scar

had to go to hospital for tetanus injection

Diaries — 2

Remember you've got to say what happened in the days after the accident as well.

What **accident** have you chosen to write about?

How did the accident **make you feel** at the time?

What were the **results** of the accident?

How many days is your diary going to cover? ....

....

*Rules for writing dramatic **diaries** are on the flap at the back.*
Read the rules — then use your plan to write a very revealing diary.

Get ☐ rules right in your diary for a free pass to Writing Wonderland.

Diaries — 3

A final, lovely diary question — what more could you want, you ungrateful so-and-so?

Write a diary about a family wedding.

You should decide:

- Who in your family is getting married
- Whether you like the person they are marrying
- What part you play in wedding preparations
- What the ceremony is like

Scribble some ideas in the boxes below to get you started.

WHO'S GETTING MARRIED

your grandmother

your sister

your cousin

your favourite uncle

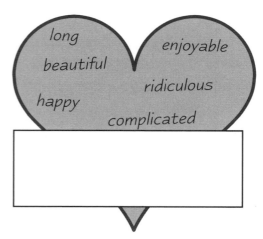

WORDS TO DESCRIBE THE PERSON THEY'RE MARRYING

ancient   friendly
funny
annoying

HOW YOU HELP WITH THE PREPARATIONS

helped make the cake

wrote wedding invitations

decorated the house for the party

WORDS TO DESCRIBE THE CEREMONY

long   enjoyable
beautiful
                ridiculous
happy
        complicated

Diaries — 3

Fill out this posh writing grid to help you with your final answer.

Who from your family is getting married? ....

....

What are **your feelings** about the person they are marrying?

What part do you play in preparing for the wedding?

What is the ceremony **like**?

*Rules for writing dramatic **diaries** are on the flap at the back.*
Read the rules — then use your plan to write a very revealing diary.

Get ☐ *rules right in your diary for a free pass to Writing Wonderland.*

Section 6 — Discussing Issues

Discussing Issues — 1

Remember — discussing things means looking at __all__ sides of the argument.

Many people think that what children see on television and at the cinema affects how they behave in real life. They think programmes such as 'Eastenders' and films such as 'Lord of the Rings' should not be shown to children at all.

Write a balanced discussion for your school newspaper that takes both sides of the argument into consideration.

You will need to decide:

• The types of programme shown on TV and the times they are shown

• The types of film children watch and how children are protected at cinemas

• The type of behaviour that might influence children

Think of loads of things to put in your discussion and write them in the boxes here.

TYPES OF PROGRAMME / FILM

thriller   horror

soap drama

comedy

HOW CHILDREN MIGHT ACT

rudeness

politeness

violence

laziness

TECHNICAL TERMS TO USE

documentary

watershed

sitcom

Parental Guidance (PG)

GOOD DISCUSSION PHRASES

However

Some people believe

On the other hand

© CGP
2003

Discussing Issues — 1

Fill in the writing frame below — but don't just write about your own opinion.

What types of **behaviour** are seen on the television and in films?

How do TV and film companies **stop** children seeing things they shouldn't? **Do** they **work**?

Who is responsible for what children see on TV and at the cinema?

....

....

*Rules for writing delectable **discussions** are on the flap at the back.*
Read the rules — then use your plan to write a discussion that blows readers away.
Get ☐ *rules right in your discussion for a free pass to Writing Wonderland.*

Discussing Issues — 2

Discussing isn't the same as arguing — you have to write about different views, not just your own.

Some people think that smoking should be banned in all public places to stop non-smokers suffering from passive smoking. Others think that this is a stupid idea.

**Write a discussion about whether it's a good idea
to ban smoking in public places or not.**

You will need to consider:

- Why smoking is bad for non-smokers

- Why smokers are likely to be against banning smoking in public areas

- Whether it would be possible to control smoking in all public areas

*Think of the opinions of smokers <u>and</u> non-smokers,
then scribble your ideas in the boxes below.*

PROBLEMS OF SMOKING IN PUBLIC AREAS

smoke stings people's eyes

makes places smelly

lung disease from passive smoking

PUBLIC AREAS

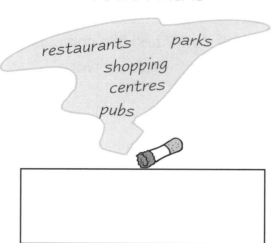

restaurants *parks*
shopping centres
pubs

TECHNICAL TERMS TO USE

nicotine *lung cancer*
tar

WAYS OF STOPPING SMOKING

go to prison *paying a fine*

have your cigarettes taken off you

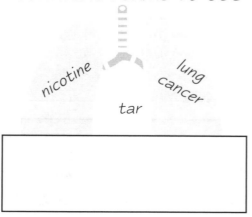

Discussing Issues — 2

Fill in the writing frame below — remember to try and use technical terms.

Why is smoking a **problem** for **non-smokers**?

What are **smokers** likely to **think** about banning smoking in public areas? **Why**?

How could you **stop** people smoking?

Would it work? **Why**?

*Rules for writing delectable **discussions** are on the flap at the back.*
Read the rules — then use your plan to write a discussion that blows readers away.

Get ☐ *rules right in your discussion for a free pass to Writing Wonderland.*

Section 6 — Discussing Issues

Discussing Issues — 3

It's the final discussion — discuss like you've never discussed before.

You and your friends have been talking about zoos. Some of them think it's wrong to keep wild animals in cages. Others think zoos are important for education and protecting endangered species of animals.

Write a discussion about whether zoos are good or bad, taking into account your friends' different views.

You will need to consider:

• Why wild animals don't like being kept in zoos

• How zoos can help protect threatened animal species

• How zoos help to educate us about animals

*Write your ideas in the boxes. Make sure you think about **all** the different views mentioned in the question.*

HOW WILD ANIMALS IN ZOOS MIGHT FEEL

bored

scared

contented

frustrated

ENDANGERED SPECIES

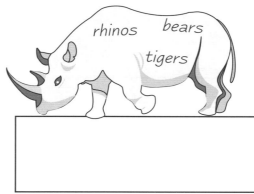

rhinos   bears

tigers

WAYS OF PROTECTING SPECIES

rescuing animals from cruelty

releasing animals into the wild

breeding programmes

THINGS ZOOS TEACH US

what noises animals make

what animals look like

where animals are from

Discussing Issues — 3

Choose your best ideas from over the page and use them to fill in this writing frame.

Why might wild animals **not like** being in a zoo?

How can zoos help **protect** endangered species?

How can zoos **teach** people about animals?

Do you think that zoos are **good** or **bad** overall?

Rules for writing delectable **discussions** are on the flap at the back.
Read the rules — then use your plan to write a discussion that blows readers away.

Get [ ] rules right in your discussion for a free pass to Writing Wonderland.

Writing About Your Point Of View — 1

Well, in my opinion, it's about time you had a go at writing about your point of view.

Vegetarians don't like eating meat. Some don't eat it because they think it is cruel whilst others just don't like the taste. Many meat eaters enjoy the flavour of meat and say it is natural to eat it because we are carnivores.

Write about your opinion on eating meat.

You will need to decide:

• Whether you agree or disagree with eating meat, and why

• Whether you are stating your opinion or persuading people to agree with you

• The type of language to use

Write down some ideas in the boxes below.
Try to think of facts to back up your point of view.

POINTS OF VIEW

it's a personal choice
strongly disagree with eating meat
think everyone needs meat in their diet

FACTS TO USE

facts about animal welfare
facts about disease
nutrition facts

GOOD PERSUASIVE WORDS

unforgivable   *innocent*
detestable
blameless

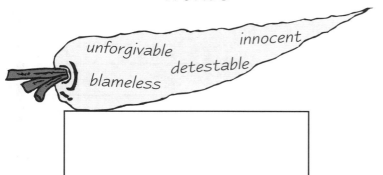

POSSIBLE TITLES

Murderous Meat

Vegetables Aren't Enough

Meat and No Veg

Writing About Your Point Of View — 1

Here's the writing frame — choose your favourite ideas and fill it in.

Do you agree or disagree with eating meat? ....

....

Three reasons for your point of view:

1.

2.

3.

Are you **stating an opinion** or **persuading** the reader? ....

....

What phrases will you use to show your point of view? ....

....

---

*Rules for writing perfect **points of view** are on the flap at the back.*
Read the rules — then use your plan to write a point of view that you can't argue with.

Get [   ] rules right in your point of view for a free pass to Writing Wonderland.

Writing About Your Point Of View — 2

See it from my point of view — practice makes perfect.

> "Living in the countryside is terrible. Towns are much better."
>
> **Do you think it's better to live in the countryside or to live in a town?**
> **Write a piece explaining your point of view on this subject.**
>
> You will need to consider:
>
> • Whether you agree or disagree with the statement
> • What your reasons are for agreeing or disagreeing
> • The type of language to use

Remember, you can say whatever you like.
It's <u>your</u> opinion that counts for this type of question.

WHAT YOU THINK

I live in town and I don't like it

I live in the countryside and I hate it

I don't think it matters where you live

FORCEFUL WORDS AND PHRASES

exciting   beautiful

unbelievably boring

peaceful   dangerous

GOOD THINGS ABOUT TOWNS

lots of shops

always new stuff happening

easy to get around

GOOD THINGS ABOUT THE COUNTRYSIDE

lots of animals

fresh air

lots to do

Writing About Your Point Of View — 2

Get everything you want to say organised here.

Do you think it's better to live in the countryside or to live in a town?

Three reasons for your point of view:

1.

2.

3.

What phrases will you use to **show** your point of view? ....

....

*Rules for writing perfect **points of view** are on the flap at the back.*
Read the rules — then use your plan to write a point of view that you can't argue with.

Get ☐ *rules right in your point of view for a free pass to Writing Wonderland.*

Writing About Your Point Of View — 3

Writing about your point of view is saying what <u>you</u> think.

Some people think dogs are great fun and good companions.

Other people think dogs are dirty, messy and dangerous.

What do you think about dogs?

Write a piece explaining your point of view.

You will need to decide:

• Whether you agree or disagree with the statement

• What your reasons are for agreeing or disagreeing

• The type of language to use

Use the boxes to decide what you think and what you're going to say about it.

WHAT YOU THINK

I love dogs and people who do not like dogs are cold-hearted monsters

dogs are a nuisance and we would be better off without them

REASONS FOR ... YOUR OPINIONS ....

small children get bitten

people living alone feel safer

they spread fleas

they're affectionate

WORDS AND PHRASES TO DESCRIBE DOGS

smelly　*loyal*

vicious

brave　*stupid*

WORDS AND PHRASES TO HELP EXPLAIN

I believe that...

Some people say...

I have noticed that...

Writing About Your Point Of View — 3

Plan exactly what you're going to say about dogs on the writing grid.

What do you think about dogs?

Four reasons for your point of view:

1.

2.

3.

4.

What phrases will you use to **show** your point of view? ....

....

*Rules for writing perfect **points of view** are on the flap at the back.*
Read the rules — then use your plan to write a point of view that you can't argue with.
Get [ ] *rules right in your point of view for a free pass to Writing Wonderland.*